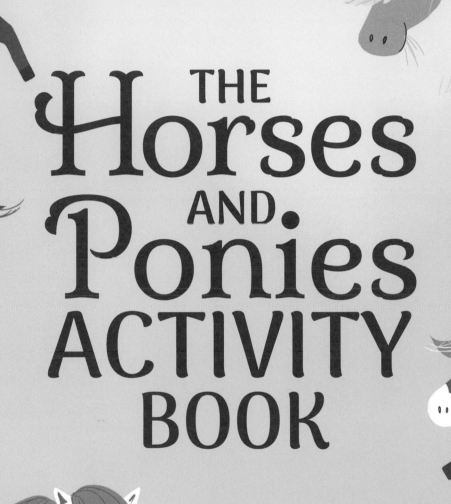

THE Horses AND Ponies ACTIVITY BOOK

ARCTURUS

ARCTURUS

This edition published in 2019 by Arcturus Publishing Limited
26/27 Bickels Yard, 151–153 Bermondsey Street,
London SE1 3HA

ISBN: 978-1-78888-483-9
CH006740NT
Supplier 29, Date 0119, Print run 7891

Author: Lisa Regan
Illustrator: Sam Loman
Editor: Becca Clunes
Designer: Well Nice Ltd

Printed in China

Home Sweet Home

This stable is home to Copper and her friends, but there are six little mice who also live here. Can you find them?

HOME TIME

What has Tilly brought home from the pony show?
Join the dots in order to find out.

Pony Prizes

Match each rider to her trophy by solving the number problems.

A $20 \div 10$

B $\frac{1}{2} + \frac{1}{2}$

C $18 - 15$

1

2

3

MY PRETTY PONY

Work out the names of the ponies by using the code key on the stable doors.

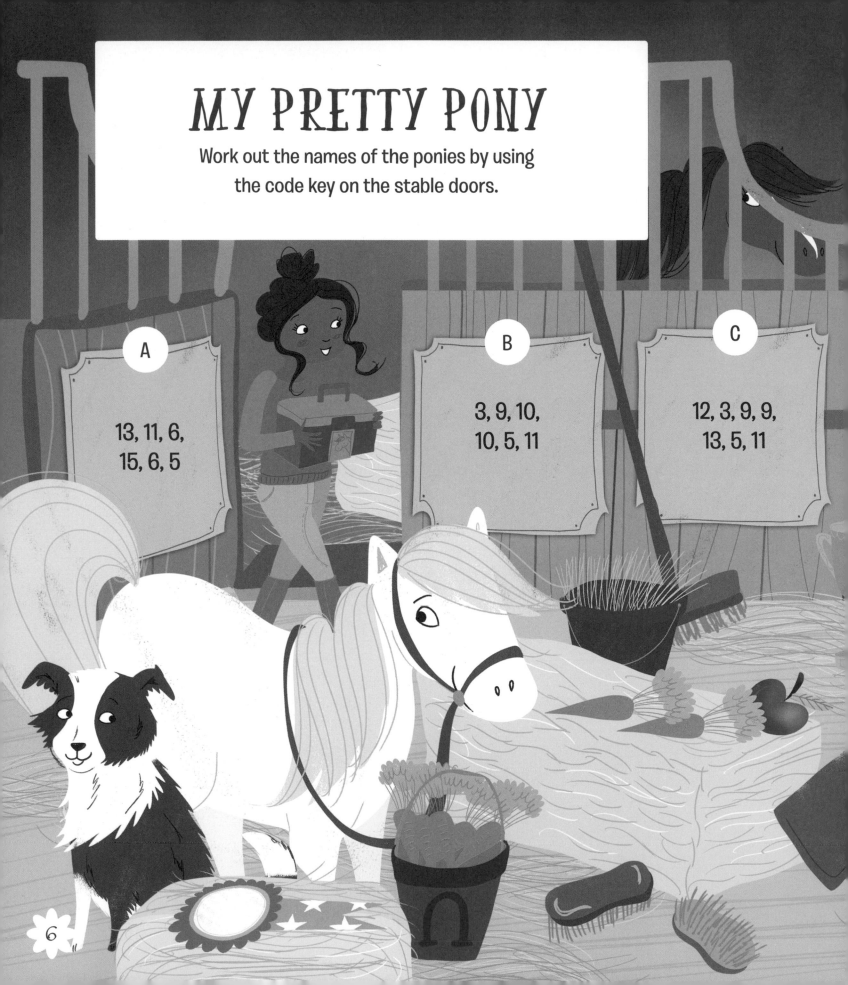

A

13, 11, 6, 15, 6, 5

B

3, 9, 10, 10, 5, 11

C

12, 3, 9, 9, 13, 5, 11

D

12, 14, 7, 4, 1,
7, 3, 5

E

3, 9, 8, 5, 13

F

12, 1, 8, 2, 1

KEY

A = 1   B = 2   C = 3   D = 4   E = 5   I = 6
N = 7   M = 8   O = 9   P = 10   R = 11   S = 12
T = 13   U = 14   X = 15

7

Pony Mane-ia

Which of the silhouettes matches the beautiful pony picture in the middle?

Amazing!

Help Scooter through the maze to reach the river.

Start

Finish

Going For Gold

Can you spot eight differences between these two show-jumping scenes?

10

Pony Puzzle

These little ones are going home with their parents after a long day at pony school. Follow the ribbons to match up each foal with its parent.

Runaway!

The ponies are grazing in the meadow, but naughty dog Bailey has escaped from his owner. Can you find him?

Draw more ducks and frogs on the pond. Add some more dragonflies, too! Now finish the scene with your pencils or crayons.

THE NAME GAME

What would you call a pony if you were lucky enough to own one?
Use the last letter of your first name, and the picture that appeals to
you the most, to find a great name.

A = Precious

B = Confetti

C = Glitter

D = Golden

E = Happy

F = Princess

G = Shimmer

H = Diamond

I = Tiny

J = Misty

K = Cutie

L = Candy

M = Fairy

N = Midnight

O = Dinky

P = Angel

Q = Rainbow

R = Buttercup

S = Twinkle

T = Moonbeam

U = Silver

V = Sugarkiss

W = Flutter

X = Dancing

Y = Peppermint

Z = Destiny

= Star

= Rainbow

= Sunlight

= Bow

= Strawberry

= Cat

= Cherry

= Sapphire

= Crown

YOUR PONY'S NAME

....

Party Tricks

Samba loves to show off her skills! Make the picture
bright and cheerful to match her mood.

Count Up

Which are there more of in the picture, bees or butterflies?

Make a Wish

Use the grid lines to help you copy this picture into the empty frame.

You Shall Go To The Ball!

Cinderella's carriage is beautifully decorated!
How many of these gems can you spot in the picture?

- [ ] Sapphires
- [ ] Rubies
- [ ] Aquamarines
- [ ] Topaz

Forest Friends

Look carefully and you will see lots of the ponies' woodland friends in this letter grid. Cross each one off the list as you find it.

R	A	B	L	L	D	M	O	L	E	E	E
R	R	O	B	R	R	E	Q	U	I	A	R
O	A	A	S	Q	U	I	R	R	E	L	A
W	B	L	T	T	R	S	O	I	E	A	R
R	B	O	I	R	H	O	B	G	E	B	E
H	I	E	M	D	G	E	I	O	G	E	A
F	T	A	O	W	L	P	N	R	I	A	E
O	P	M	U	O	S	S	E	I	L	R	E
X	O	S	S	A	D	M	O	U	S	A	R
S	Q	U	E	I	R	D	E	E	R	R	H
B	I	T	B	B	A	H	E	D	G	A	E
M	H	E	D	G	E	H	O	G	O	E	D

RABBIT   **MOUSE**   **OWL**   **HEDGEHOG**   **MOLE**
SQUIRREL   **ROBIN**   **DEER**   **BEAR**   **FOX**

Getting Busy

There are lots of activities and games to do on horseback.
Unscramble the groups of letters to find six fun things to do.

A LOOP

B NIMGUPJ

C CARGIN

D nackhgi

E GEARSEDS

F LAVUNITG

21

Saddle Up

Use the clues to find out which pony belongs to each of the riders.

Mia's horse is not in the middle.

Moonlight and Mocha are on the left and right.

Rachel owns Misty.

Poppy's horse is white.

Mocha's forelock does not cover her eyes.

Oodles of Doodles

Make these ponies as pretty as a picture using pencils and crayons.

ABOUT FACE

Decode the numbers to find out the name of each pony's type of face marking.

A

12, 13, 1, 11

B

12, 8, 6, 10

C

12, 13, 11, 6, 10, 3

D

2, 7, 1, 15, 3

KEY

A = 1   B = 2   E = 3   F = 4   G = 5   I = 6
L = 7   N = 8   O = 9   P = 10   R = 11   S = 12
T = 13   U = 14   Z = 15

24

Yee-haw!

Only one of the silhouettes is an exact match for the cowgirl and her pony.
Which one?

A

B

C

D

On the Road

The ponies have to travel to their next big show, and they're doing it in style!
Which of the five horse boxes is slightly different from the others?

1

2

3

4

5

Remember, Remember

Lexie's bedroom is full to bursting with pony items.
Take a good look, and then turn the page to test how much you can remember.

A Home for Sparkle

Try to answer the questions without turning back to the main picture.

1. Is the lamp pink or blue?

2. How many cups has Lexie won?

3. Can you see Lexie's riding boots?

4. There is a unicorn on Lexie's pillow—true or false?

5. What decoration is not on the duvet—stars, hearts, or diamonds?

6. How many toy ponies are on the shelf?

7. There is a cat asleep on the bed. What toy animals are there, too?

8. Lexie's slippers look like rabbits—true or false?

9. What is the title of the book?

10. There is a rosette on the wall—true or false?

Now You See Me...

Which of the animals has wandered off in the second picture?

Trixie Time!

Trixie the little white pony is waiting for her owner. Use the letters to spell her name. Is it Emilia, Milly, Mylia, or Emily?

E

I

L

M

Y

LUCKY FOR SOME

Look carefully to find a four-leaf clover in front of Scooter and Sundance's field.

CRUNCH TIME

Which are there more of on this page, carrots or apples?

Your Turn

Follow the simple steps to learn how to draw a cute pony.

Big Is Beautiful

How many new words can you make using the letters in SHIRE HORSE?

SHIRE HORSE

34

Feeling Lucky?

Can you find the lucky horseshoe in this collection?
It looks like the one in the frame.

Pony Trekking

Keep your eyes peeled when you're out on a trek. You could see lots of creatures. Find the ones in the picture list below.

37

Training Test

Which of the lead ropes is attached to the pony?

Be an Artist

Use this picture to help you draw your own beautiful pony and carriage.
Copy it carefully into the space, and finish it with your pens or crayons.

HEADING FOR HOME

Which pony has to travel the farthest to reach home?
Add up the numbers on each trail to find out.

9

6

7

3

8

5

1

2

4

3

9

7

2

10

1

7

2

7

4

A

B

C

Jump to It!

Which route out of the maze passes over exactly six jumps?

Start

Finish

WHATEVER THE WEATHER

Misty is having a lovely time in the snow!
How many times can you find her name hidden in the grid?

M	I	S	T	Y	M	M	I	T	Y
T	Y	I	I	Y	Y	S	T	M	M
M	M	M	I	S	T	Y	M	I	M
M	S	T	Y	I	S	M	I	S	I
T	I	M	I	S	T	Y	Y	T	Y
Y	S	S	S	M	I	T	Y	Y	S
Y	I	M	T	T	S	I	S	Y	I
I	T	T	S	Y	M	I	S	Y	T
T	M	I	S	T	Y	T	I	S	M
I	S	Y	T	M	M	I	S	T	Y

Jump Around

Count up in twos to make sure you complete the jumps in the correct order.

A Sunny Day

The meadow is full of wildlife. Among them are four
blue diamond-winged butterflies. Can you find them?

45

Pretty Things

Which are there more of, pink flowers or white ones?

The Olden Days

The knights of old relied on their faithful horses to see them safely through a battle.
Finish this scene with your crayons or pens.

Shaken Up

Which of the snow globes is the odd one out?

I LOVE MY PONY

Finish the picture with pencils or crayons. Add more hearts and flowers.

A PONY PROBLEM

Study the pictures and figure out which order they should be in to tell the story.

It All Adds Up

Fill in the missing numbers (from 1 to 9) so that each row, column, and diagonal adds up to 15.

A Big Day Out

Study the scene and find each of the items on the picture list.

Best Breeds

Use the grid references to work out the breed of horse each rider likes the best.

Let's Celebrate!

Which of the puzzle pieces complete the party picture?

Say What?

Unscramble the horsey words and match them to the correct meaning.

CLOT LOAF REAM LILYF LIONLAST

1. A male horse over 4 years old.

2. A male horse under 4 years old.

3. A baby horse or pony.

4. A female horse over 4 years old.

5. A female horse under 4 years old.

Your Turn

Follow the simple steps to learn how to draw a cute pony.

NUMBER MATCH

Work out the number problems to find which pony should be in each horse carrier.

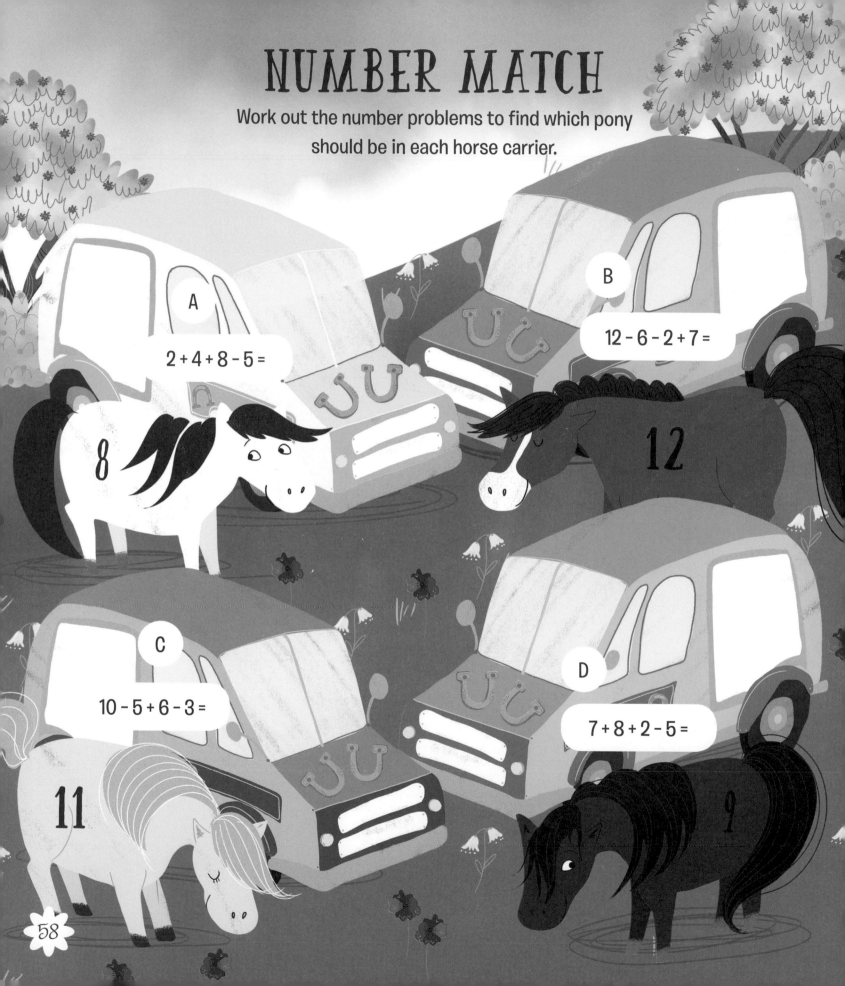

A
2 + 4 + 8 - 5 =

B
12 - 6 - 2 + 7 =

C
10 - 5 + 6 - 3 =

D
7 + 8 + 2 - 5 =

8

12

11

9

Remember, Remember

Look at this picture for a few minutes and then turn the page to see how many questions you can answer from memory.

Remember, Remember

Try to answer the questions without looking back at the picture.

1. Is it a full moon?

2. How many people are in the picture?

3. How many ponies are in the picture?

4. What is the girl with the pony tail doing?

5. There is a bear in the picture—true or false?

6. The spotted horse's rug is yellow—true or false?

7. There is a deer in the picture—true or false?

8. How many fireflies are there?

9. Both horses are asleep—true or false?

10. The children are wearing riding helmets—true or false?

It's a Shoe Thing

Can you find this pattern of horseshoes concealed in the grid?
Look left to right, not diagonally or backward.

Two Many

Cross out any letter that appears twice.
Use the leftover letters to spell a breed of horse.

APLSFHO
OPIRAFEL

_ _ _ _ _

Sitting Pretty

It's best to ride sidesaddle if you're a princess on a pony!
Copy this picture and finish it with crayons.

Charming!

Which of the bracelet charms do you like the most?
See what it says about your personality.

1

You can be a worrier, and feel safest when you have a plan to follow. You will do whatever you can to make sure that the people you love are happy. This makes you a loyal and caring friend.

2

It's not that you're competitive but ... why isn't this choice the first one?! You do love to win, but you are fair and would never, ever break the rules. You can't bear cheating or lying.

3

You like the finer things in life, and will work hard and save your money to get the very best. You want people to think the best of you, and always take care with your appearance.

4

Everyone loves your down-to-earth attitude. You are practical and can be relied upon to get things done. You love to dress up, but are just as happy mucking out, if that's what's needed.

5

You're an outdoors person who is happiest in the summer, and feels cooped up in the bad weather. You never sit still, and always have a dozen different projects on the go. It's okay to chill, you know?

6

Dare we say it ... you can be a bit of a princess? You always follow fashion, and can't bear to wait for something if you really, really want it. Your friends love you, but know that you can be demanding sometimes.

Horse Talk

Look for each of the horse-related words hidden in the grid.

WALK   CANTER   GAIT   GROOM   REINS

TROT   GALLOP   STABLE   FARRIER   STIRRUP

F	A	R	R	I	E	R	S	G	P
A	S	T	A	B	L	E	R	R	I
L	W	A	L	K	A	I	S	O	A
O	S	T	A	B	L	N	O	O	M
T	F	A	R	R	I	S	R	M	S
R	E	G	A	L	L	O	P	O	P
O	G	A	R	R	U	P	T	R	O
T	R	I	C	A	N	T	E	R	S
T	A	T	B	L	E	R	R	I	E
O	W	S	T	I	R	R	U	P	W

66

That's the One

Can you find Aston in this group of ponies?
He has a white coat and a golden mane and tail.

By The River

Sally the shire horse is pulling the boat along the canal.
Caramel the cat is watching. Can you see her?

Now finish the scene with your pencils and crayons.

Over We Go

Which of the silhouettes is an exact match for the clever pony in the middle?

It's Your Year

If you (or a family member or friend) were born in 1954, 1966, 1978, 1990, 2002, or 2014 then you were born in the Chinese year of the horse.

These people are lively, energetic, and full of enthusiasm. They are fun to be with and have lots of friends. They are positive thinkers, good at working on their own, and will keep going until a task is finished. They do love to spend money, though! Their worst aspect is not being able to keep a secret.

Their lucky numbers are 2, 3, and 7, and their lucky flowers are calla lilies, jasmine, and marigolds.

These people should choose purple, yellow, and brown.

Do you know any horse people?

Trick or Treat?

What a fun way to spend Halloween! Finish the puzzle with the correct pieces.

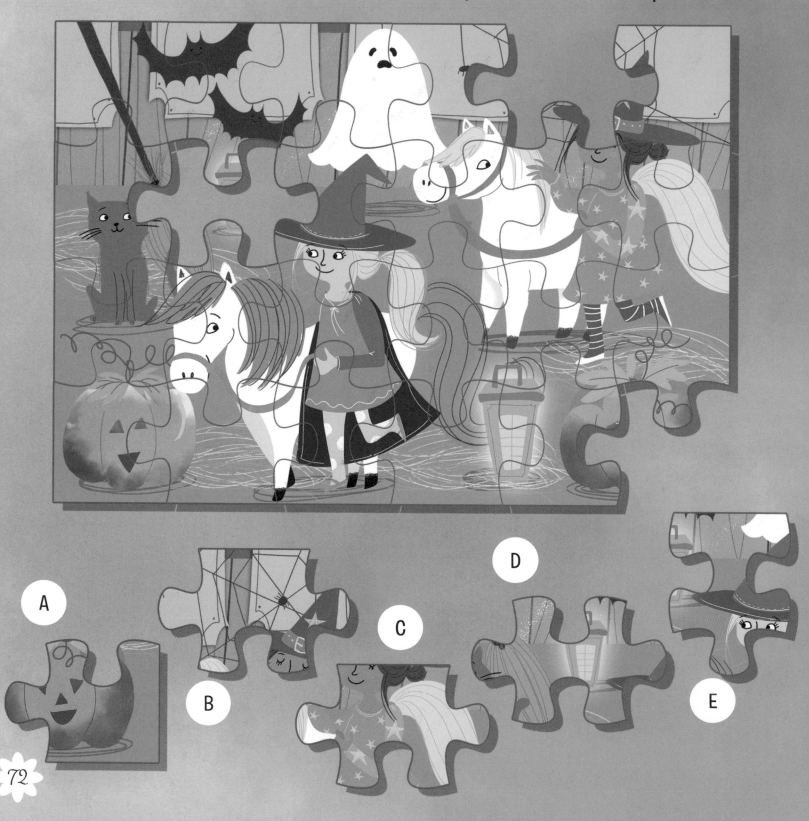

Wordsmith

How many words can you make using the letters from THOROUGHBRED?
Write them down as you think of them.

THOROUGHBRED

Bet Your Boots!

Stacey is choosing new boots. Which ones does she decide to buy?

A

B

C

She wants boots with stars but she doesn't like red stripes. She would prefer boots with a white heel because they look stylish. She thinks boots look better if they have three stars as a decoration.

D

E

F

74

Four-legged Friend

Shade in the sections that contain a number from the four times table to reveal the hidden shape.

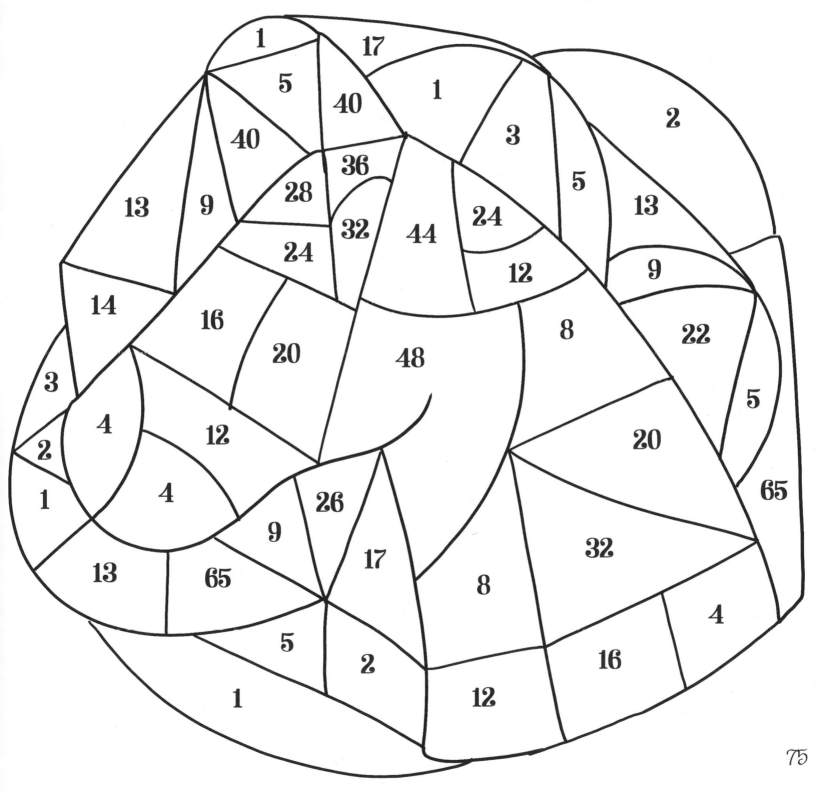

FLYING HIGH

Which bird will land on the branch above Sundance's head?

A

B

C

Finish

Food-oku!

Fill in the blanks so that each row, column,
and mini-grid has one of each type of snack.

FOALING AROUND

How many butterflies and caterpillars
can you find in this picture?

A Different Ride

Climb up onto these fairground ponies!
Finish the scene to make it bright and fun.

Hidden Hooves

How many times can you find the word HOOF hidden in this grid?
Look forward and down, but not diagonally.

O	O	H	H	O	F	F	H	H	O
F	H	O	O	O	F	H	H	O	F
H	O	H	O	O	F	O	O	O	H
H	H	O	O	O	H	O	F	F	F
H	H	O	F	H	O	H	O	O	O
F	O	F	F	O	H	O	O	F	F
H	O	F	F	H	O	F	F	H	H
F	F	O	H	O	O	H	F	O	H
H	O	H	F	H	O	O	O	F	H
O	H	F	F	O	H	O	O	F	F

Wild Wild West

Help the cowgirl through the maze to meet up with her trusty steed. She can't push past any prickly cacti.

Finish

Start

Spotted!

Which of the Appaloosa ponies is a tiny bit different from the others?

As If By Magic

Follow the steps to create your own pumpkin carriage,
even if you don't have a fairy godmother!

Happy Days

Reverse the letters of the alphabet to work out what this message says.
Fill in the key to figure it out.

UVVORMT WLDM?
HZWWOV FK!

A	B	C	D	E	F							
Z	Y	X										

Stable Mates

Match each of the adorable stable mice into pairs.
Which one is on its own?

RACING FINISH

Shade in all the boxes with the letters from the word GALLOP
to reveal the name of a famous racecourse.

G	A	L	L	O	P	O	P	G	O
A	G	A	L	L	O	P	G	A	L
G	K	L	L	O	P	G	A	L	G
L	G	A	E	A	P	L	L	A	
G	G	A	L	L	O	P	N	O	L
A	G	A	L	L	O	P	O	P	L
T	G	A	L	U	O	P	P	O	A
G	A	L	L	O	P	C	A	L	O
O	A	G	A	L	L	K	P	P	O
P	L	O	P	G	A	L	L	Y	P

Riders' Gear

Each piece of equipment is worth a different number. When they are added across or down, they equal the total in the circle. Which piece of equipment is missing?

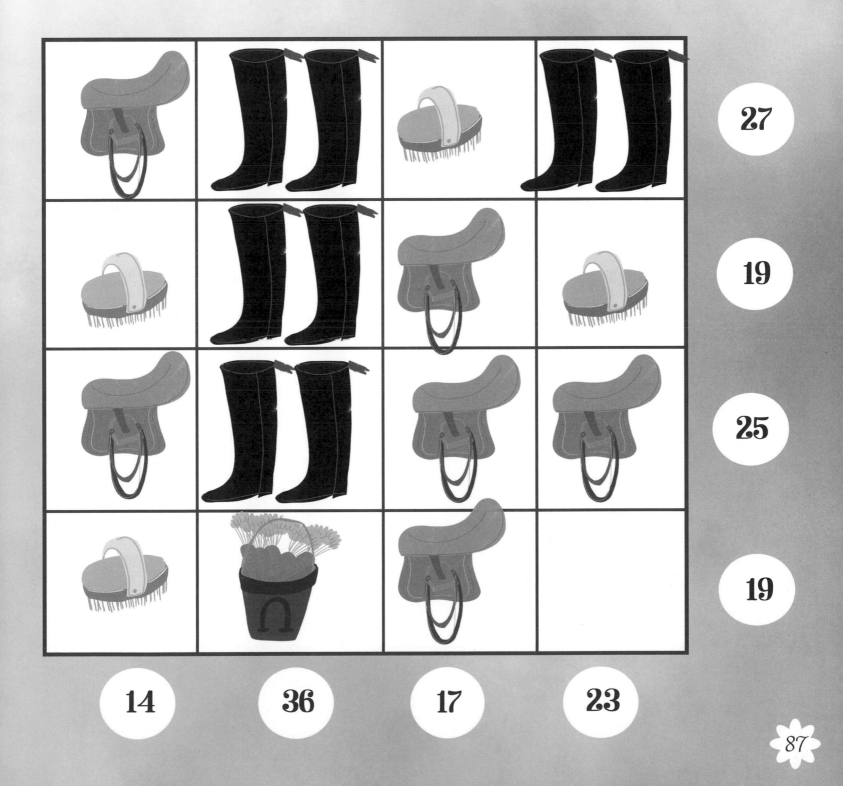

A New Arrival

A new pony has arrived. Can you draw her in?

Answers

Page 3

Page 5

A = $20 \div 10$ → 2

B = $\frac{1}{2} + \frac{1}{2}$ → 1

C = $18 - 15$ → 3

Page 8

Page 4

Pages 6-7

A = TRIXIE

B = COPPER

C = SCOOTER

D = SUNDANCE

E = COMET

F = SAMBA

Page 9

Answers

Page 10

Page 11

1 = C

2 = A

3 = B

Pages 12-13

Page 16

There are more BUTTERFLIES.

BEES = 17

BUTTERFLIES = 23

Page 18-19

5 Sapphires

5 Rubies

3 Aquamarines

4 Topaz

Page 20

R	A	B	L	L	D	M	O	L	E	E	E
R	R	O	B	R	R	E	Q	U	I	A	R
O	A	A	S	Q	U	I	R	R	E	L	A
W	B	L	T	T	R	S	O	I	E	A	R
R	B	O	I	R	H	O	B	G	E	B	E
H	I	E	M	D	G	E	I	O	G	E	A
F	T	A	O	W	L	P	N	R	I	A	E
O	P	M	U	O	S	S	E	I	L	R	E
X	O	S	S	A	D	M	O	U	S	A	R
S	Q	U	E	I	R	D	E	E	R	R	R
B	I	T	B	B	A	H	E	D	G	A	E
M	H	E	D	G	E	H	O	G	O	E	D

Page 21

A = POLO

B = JUMPING

C = RACING

D = HACKING

E = DRESSAGE

F = VAULTING

Page 22

A = MOCHA IS MIA'S PONY

B = MISTY IS RACHEL'S PONY

C = MOONLIGHT IS POPPY'S PONY

Page 24

A = STAR

B = SNIP

C = STRIPE

D = BLAZE

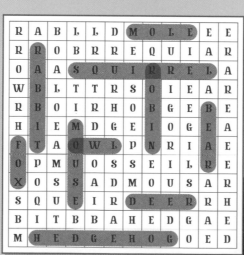

Answers

Page 25

Page 26

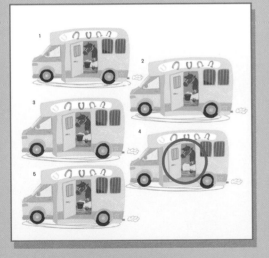

Pages 27-28

1. The lamp is pink.

2. Lexie has won one cup.

3. Yes, you can see her riding boots.

4. False. It is a pony.

5. There are no diamonds on her duvet.

6. There are three toy ponies on the shelf.

7. A unicorn and a rabbit.

8. False. Her slippers are horses, of course!

9. The book is called *A Home for Sparkle*.

10. True. Her rosette is yellow.

Page 29

Page 30

EMILY

Page 31

Page 32

There are more APPLES.

APPLES = 23

CARROTS = 17

Page 34

Here are a few that you can make: ROSE, SIR, HERO, SORE, HISS, HER, HOSE, SHE, HIS, SHOE, SHORE.

If you found HEIRESS, be very proud of yourself!

Answers

Page 35

Page 38

Page 41

Page 36

Page 42

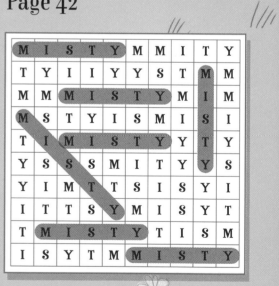

Page 40

The horse that has the farthest to travel is B with 34.

A. 6 + 3 + 4 + 9 + 2 + 2 = 26

B. 5 + 8 + 1 + 3 + 10 + 7 = 34

C. 9 + 7 + 2 + 7 + 1 + 4 = 30

Answers

Page 43

Page 44-45

Page 46

There are more WHITE flowers.

WHITE = 22

PINK = 13

Page 48

Page 50

To tell the story, the pictures should be in this order: 4, 3, 2, 1.

Page 51

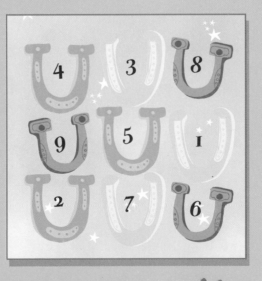

Page 52-53

Page 54

1. HOLSTEINER

2. LIPIZZANER

3. ARABIAN

4. APPALOOSA

Page 55

Answers

Page 56

STALLION = A male horse over 4 years old.

COLT = A male horse under 4 years old.

FOAL = A baby horse or pony.

MARE = A female horse over 4 years old.

FILLY = A female horse under 4 years old.

Page 58

A. 2 + 4 + 8 − 5 = 9

B. 12 − 6 − 2 + 7 = 11

C. 10 − 5 + 6 − 3 = 8

D. 7 + 8 + 2 − 5 = 12

Pages 59-60

1. No, it's not a full moon.

2. There are two people.

3. There are two ponies.

4. She is toasting a marshmallow.

5. False. There is no bear.

6. False. Its rug is red.

7. True. There is a deer in the picture.

8. There are six fireflies.

9. False. One is awake.

10. False. They are not wearing their helmets.

Page 61

Page 62

APLSFHO OPIRAFEL

S H I R E

Page 66

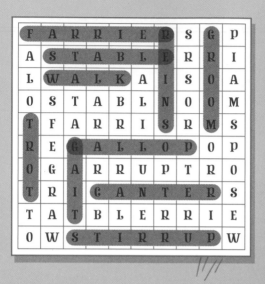

Page 67

Answers

Pages 68-69

Page 70

Page 72

Page 73

You might have found these words:

TUBE, DOOR, BED, RUG, TOE, BORED, ORDER, RODEO, HURT, TRUE, GOOD, BOOT.

Page 74

1. They are mostly brown.
2. There are no stripes on them.
3. They don't have stars.
4. The foot is not black.
5. They have a black band at the top.

Page 75

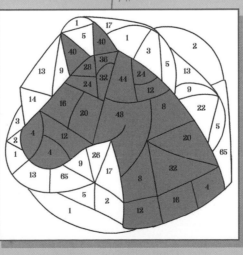

Page 76

Page 77

Page 78

BUTTERFLIES = 16

CATERPILLARS = 13

Answers

Page 80

Page 81

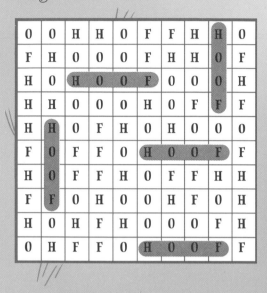

Page 82

Page 84

FEELING DOWN? SADDLE UP!

Page 85

Page 86

The racecourse is
KENTUCKY.

Page 87

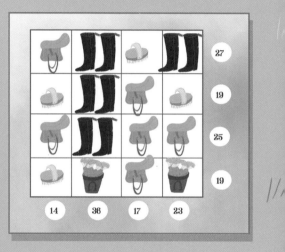